OT THE ROBOT

plays the game

Jim Carrington  Juanbjuan Oliver

Otis the Robot plays the game
ISBN: 978-1-85503-606-2

© Jim Carrington 2017
Illustrations by Juanbjuan Oliver / Beehive

This edition published 2017
10 9 8 7 6 5 4 3 2 1

Printed in the UK by Page Bros (Norwich) Ltd
Designed and typeset by Andy Wilson for Green Desert Ltd

LDA, Findel Education, 2 Gregory Street, Hyde, Cheshire SK14 4HR

www.ldalearning.com

The right of Jim Carrington to be identified as the author of this work has been asserted in accordance with Sections 77 and 78 of the Copyright, Designs and Patents Act 1988.

Hi! My name is Otis. I am a robot.

I go to Roboschool every day
except weekends, holidays
and when I'm ill.

Today, Mrs A-Bot let me and Marvin choose a game to play after we finished our work.

I like playing games.
I chose my favourite game
in the whole world:

Marvin went first. '4.'

I rolled a 2. Up a ladder!

Marvin's go. '5.'
His counter landed on
the head of a robosnake.

He had to
go back to
the start.

40

38

1

I **smiled.** My circuits felt **warm** and **happy.** I was winning!

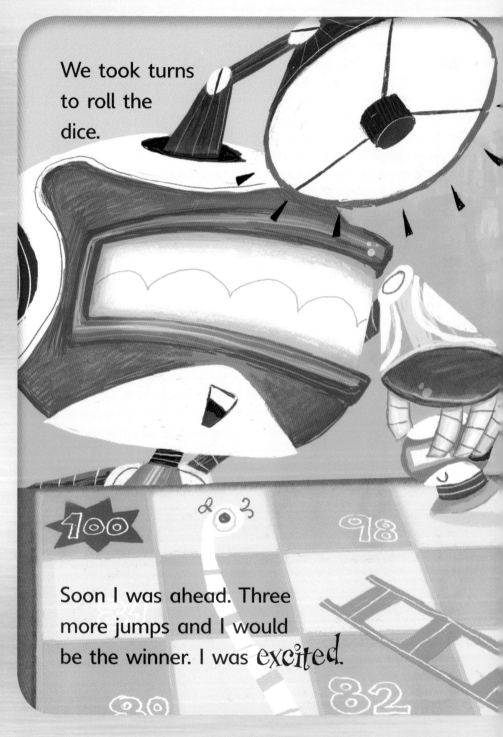

We took turns
to roll the
dice.

Soon I was ahead. Three
more jumps and I would
be the winner. I was *excited.*

I rolled a 2.
I moved my counter forward.
'One . . . two.'

I had to go almost
all the way back
to the start.

My circuits started to feel **fizzy** because I thought I was going to lose. I felt **ANGRY**.

'This game is **stupid!**'
I shouted.

Mrs A-Bot came
to find me.
'Let's read
The Manual,'
she said.

'It has a page about staying calm when you're playing a game.'

how to stay calm when i play a game

'Shall we try again?' she asked.

This time we finished
the game.

Marvin won.
My circuits started
to feel **fizzy** again.

But I counted to ten
and took deep breaths.

'Well done, Marvin,' I said.
'You're the winner.'

Marvin *smiled.*
That made me feel
like a winner too.

How to stay calm when you play a game

(from Otis the Robot plays the game)

I like playing games because it's fun.

My friends like to play games. They think it is fun too.

Sometimes I win the game and I'm happy.

Sometimes someone else wins the game. It makes them happy too.

I might feel angry if I don't win. Children don't like it when someone shouts or is unkind to them because they didn't win a game.

If I lose a game, I can remember that it's not so bad. Another time I might win.

If I feel angry, I can count to ten or take deep breaths. This usually helps me calm down.

We can all say 'well done' to the winner of the game. This is great.